Play-along for Trumpet

TODAY'S
SHOWSTOPPERS!

Published by
Wise Publications
14-15 Berners Street, London W1T 3LJ, UK.

Exclusive Distributors:
Music Sales Limited
Distribution Centre, Newmarket Road, Bury St Edmunds,
Suffolk IP33 3YB, UK.
Music Sales Pty Limited
120 Rothschild Avenue, Rosebery, NSW 2018, Australia.

Order No. AM1001506
ISBN 13: 978-1-84938-677-7
This book © Copyright 2010 Wise Publications,
a division of Music Sales Limited.

Top line arrangements by Chris Hussey.
Engraving supplied by Camden Music.
Backing tracks by John Maul,
except 'Suddenly Seymour' by Danny Gluckstein.
Edited by Lizzie Moore.

CD recorded, mixed and mastered by Jonas Persson.
Trumpet played by Andy Gathercole.

Printed in the EU.

Play-along for Trumpet
TODAY'S
SHOWSTOPPERS!

Wise Publications
part of The Music Sales Group
LONDON / NEW YORK / PARIS / SYDNEY / COPENHAGEN / BERLIN / MADRID / HONG KONG / TOKYO

Trumpet Fingering Chart

MOUTHPIECE

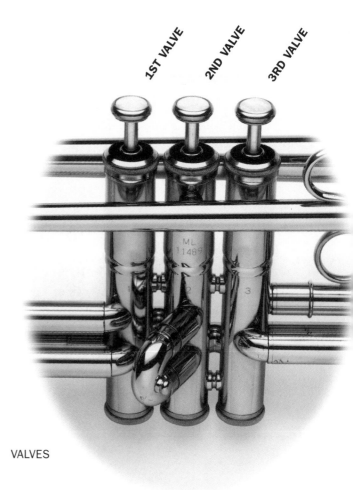

VALVES

1ST VALVE   2ND VALVE   3RD VALVE

SOUNDS

Bb TRUMPET / CORNET / FLUGELHORN:
e | f | f#/gb | g | g#/ab | a | a#/bb | b | c¹ | c#¹/db¹ | d¹ | d#¹/eb¹ | e¹ | f¹ | f#¹/gb¹ | g¹

BARITONE:
E | F | F#/Gb | G | G#/Ab | A | A#/Bb | B | c | c#/db | d | d#/eb | e | f | f#/gb | g

WRITTEN

f#/gb | g | g#/ab | a | a#/bb | b | c¹ | c#¹/db¹ | d¹ | d#¹/eb¹ | e¹ | f¹ | f#¹/gb¹ | g¹ | g#¹/ab¹ | a¹

RIGHT HAND

Indicates the lower limit of the best playing range

Transposition

The B♭ trumpet, cornet and flugelhorn
sound a major second below the written pitch.
Rule: **Written C sounds B♭**

Written:    Sounds:

The baritone sounds a major ninth below
the written pitch. Rule: **Written C sounds B♭**

Written:    Sounds:

Pitch System

The letter names which appear at the top of the
fingering chart indicate the relative octave as well as
the name of each pitch, as shown below.

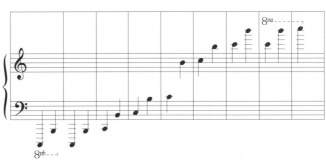

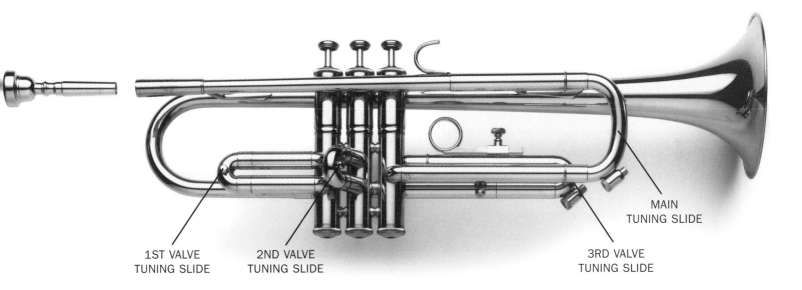

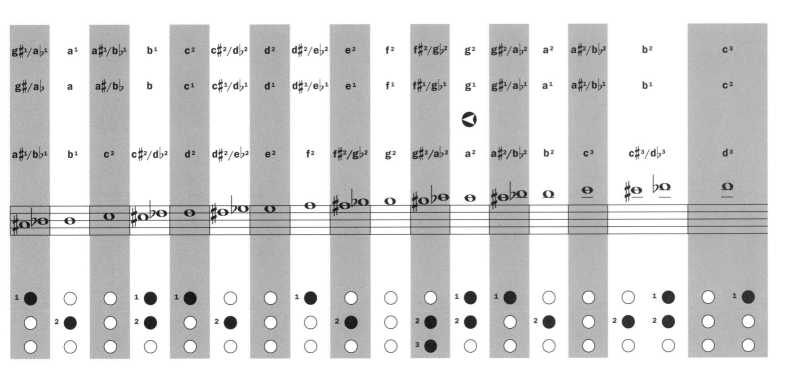

◄ Indicates the upper limit of the best playing range

Defying Gravity
(from 'Wicked')

Words & Music by Stephen Schwartz

Expressively ♩ = 76

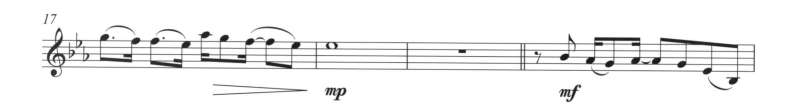

Good Morning Baltimore
(from 'Hairspray')

Words & Music by Marc Shaiman & Scott Wittman

Brightly, with a bounce ♩ = 132

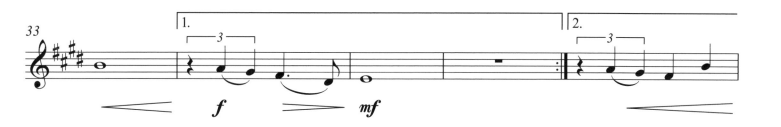

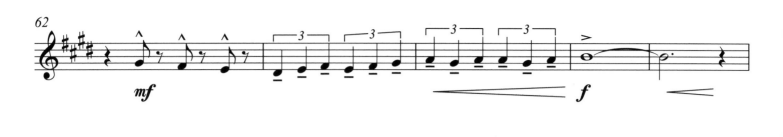

molto rit.

Honey, Honey
(from 'Mamma Mia!')

Words & Music by Benny Andersson, Stig Anderson & Björn Ulvaeus

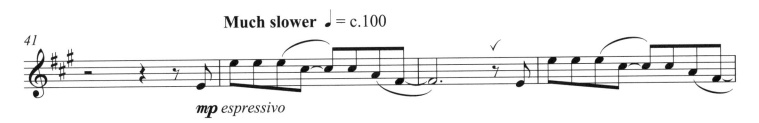

The Letter
(from 'Billy Elliot: The Musical')

Words by Lee Hall & Music by Elton John

Love Never Dies
(from 'Love Never Dies')

Music by Andrew Lloyd Webber

Expressively ♩ = 129

(strings cue)

Più mosso ♩ = 80

molto rit.   **A tempo** ♩ = 130

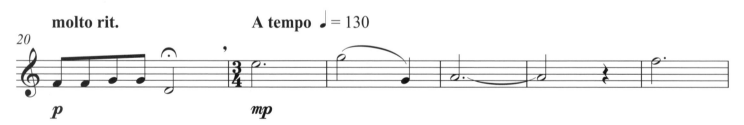

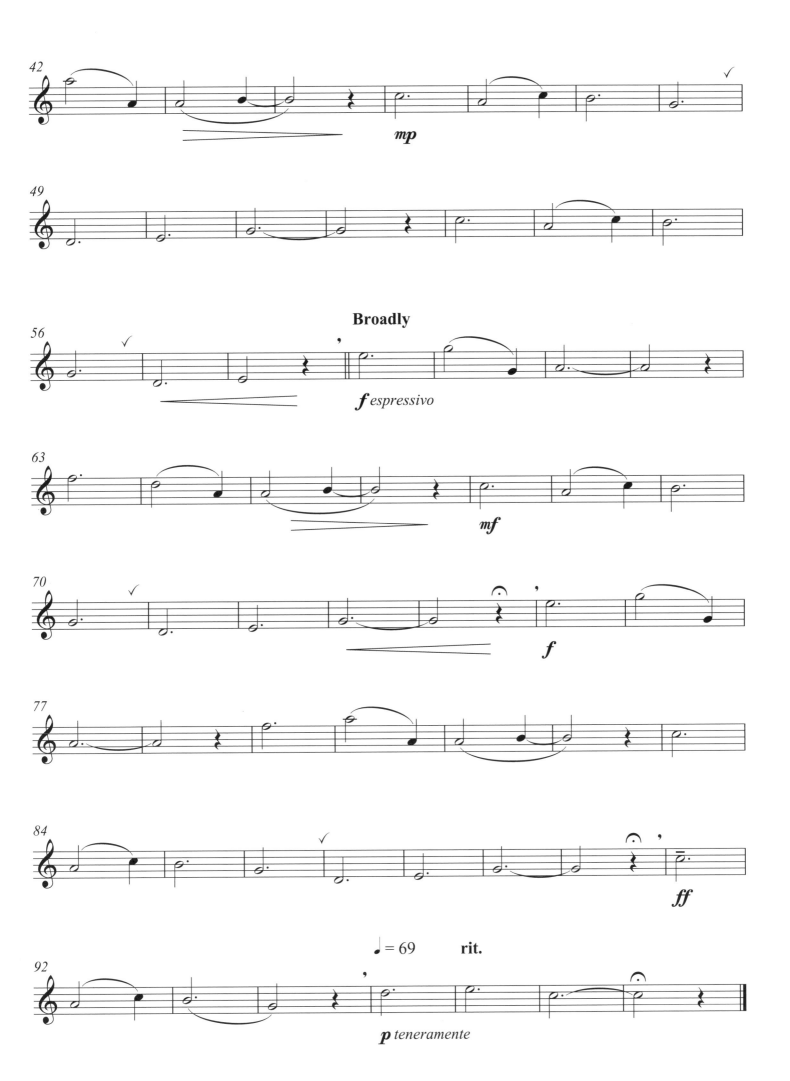

Seasons Of Love
(from 'Rent')

Words & Music by Jonathan Larson

Rhythmically ♩ = 89

(piano cue)

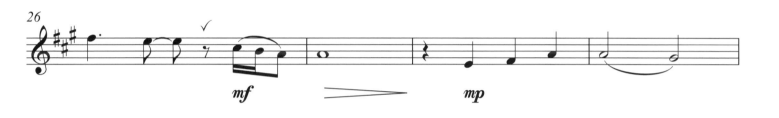

20

Suddenly Seymour
(from 'Little Shop Of Horrors')

Words by Howard Ashman
Music by Alan Menken

A little faster ♩ = 102

mf ritmico

f

mp

22

Tell Me It's Not True
(from 'Blood Brothers')

Words & Music by Willy Russell

Smoothly ♩ = 72

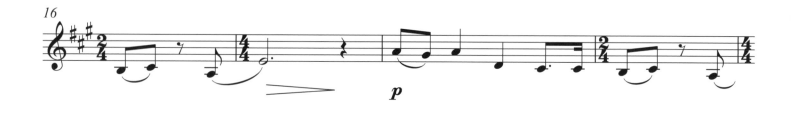

We Belong

(from 'Priscilla: Queen Of The Desert—The Musical')

Words & Music by Daniel Navarro & David Eric Lowen

Powerfully ♩ = 135

Working My Way Back To You
(from 'Jersey Boys')

Words & Music by Sandy Linzer & Denny Randell

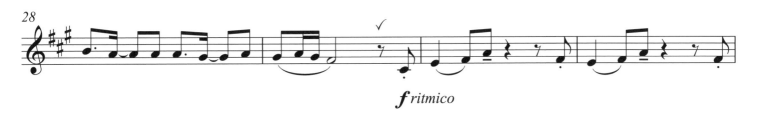

f *ritmico*

mf

f

ff

CD Track Listing

Full instrumental performances...

1. Tuning notes
2. Defying Gravity
   (Schwartz) Greydog Music
3. Good Morning Baltimore
   (Shaiman/Wittman) Songs of Pen UK
4. Honey, Honey
   (Andersson/Anderson/Ulvaeus) Bocu Music Limited
5. The Letter
   (Hall/John) Universal Music Publishing Limited
6. Love Never Dies
   (Webber) The Really Useful Group Limited
7. Seasons Of Love
   (Larson) Universal/MCA Music Limited
8. Suddenly Seymour
   (Ashman/Menken) Universal/MCA Music Limited/
   Warner/Chappell North America Limited
9. Tell Me It's Not True
   (Russell) W. R. Limited
10. We Belong
    (Navarro/Lowen) Screen Gems-EMI Music Limited
11. Working My Way Back To You
    (Linzer/Randell) Screen Gems-EMI Music Limited/EMI Music Publishing Limited

Backing tracks only...

12. Defying Gravity
13. Good Morning Baltimore
14. Honey, Honey
15. The Letter
16. Love Never Dies
17. Seasons Of Love
18. Suddenly Seymour
19. Tell Me It's Not True
20. We Belong
21. Working My Way Back To You

To remove your CD from the plastic sleeve,
lift the small lip to break the perforations.
Replace the disc after use for convenient storage